WRITTEN BY
Neshawne Gibson

ILLUSTRATED BY
Whimsical Designs by CJ

To my 3 musketeers –

Thank you for being the inspiration behind this book. I hope the knowledge and tools daddy and I give you, will empower you to do far more than your heart's desire! Pass on your HBCU knowledge to others for generations to come. Know you are way more powerful beyond your belief. Trust in yourself. Trust in God. I love you all mostest!

To my mother and father –

Thank you for teaching me as a child about our rich history. Ma, you were a first generation HBCU grad and paved the way for me to go to college. Not just any college, your alma mater, my alma mater, NCCU, an HBCU. Eagle Pride! You and daddy's tenacity, perseverance, grace, and love made me into the woman I am today. Look mama, I made it!
I pray I make you both proud!

To my husband –

Thank you for all of your continued patience, unconditional love and support. I love you always and forever babe!

What do you want to be when you grow up? You can be whatever you want to be.

Just pray, listen to your heart, Work hard, and you'll see the possibilities.

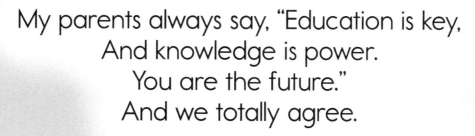

My parents always say, "Education is key,
And knowledge is power.
You are the future."
And we totally agree.

Hi, I'm Mason,
And this is my sister, Mia.
We are twins, but I'm the oldest.
It's quite nice to meet ya.

Today, we're going on an adventure.
Mom and Dad included.
It's time to go!
We're all suited and booted.

HOMECOMING

We are in the car, traveling a bit far
To Mom and Dad's school
For the yearly HBCU celebration called Homecoming.
Ooh wee, I can't wait. It's going to be so cool!

The food, the music,
The parade, and shows!

The football game,
the band, and dancers.

It's going to be epic. We can't wait to go!

Right now, Mia and I are in elementary school.
Next is middle school, then high school graduation.
After that, we're off to college.
Oh, what a special occasion!

What is college?
You may ask.

It's where you go to grow,
learn, and build your future.

But it's no easy task.

We have the same talk
Every year during our car ride.
My parents tell us how important education is
And remind us of our history, so rich with pride.

Dad said, "To go to college,
You have to be a hard worker.
Do your homework, and be responsible.
There's no time for jokers."

Mom said, "We have many choices to find our true voices
With all of the different schools near and far.
But there are some schools called HBCUs
That raised the learning bar."

Mom and Dad graduated from an HBCU.
They sure are smart and bright.
When I grow up, I want to be just like them
So I can put my stamp on the world and shine my light.

What's an HBCU? You may be wondering.
It's not just any ol' college.
It's a place where I see people who look just like me:
Smart, black, and educated with lots and lots of knowledge.

HBCU stands for Historically Black College or University
And each one started before 1964
To allow black students to learn and go to school
So they can experience more…

More equality.
More opportunity.
More jobs.
All for our community.

A long time ago, black people were not allowed go to most schools.
But after the Civil War, there was a new rule,
A law called The Higher Education Act of 1965.
Allowing equal education for every American, so we all can thrive.

I know all about HBCUs
Because my parents always teach us about our history.
We do fun projects and talk about our future
So the past won't be a mystery.

HIGHER EDUCATION
ACT OF 1965
To strengthen the educational resources of our
colleges and universities and to provide
financial assistance for students in
postsecondary and higher education

Mom and Dad chit chatter for almost an hour
About HBCU highs and lows.
By that time, I saw the school's sign
And knew we made it. "Dad, hurry! Let's go!"

"We made it, we made it. We're here!"
Sis and I said with joy.
We hopped out of the car, doing our dance.
"Yeaaaaa boooyy!"

Mia turned with excitement. "The parade just started.
And look, there goes the King and Queen!"
I picture Mia and I on the float
As happy as jumping jelly beans!

Homecoming is a celebration of the school
And black history as a whole.

Where old and new students have fun together and spread love
Through parades, dance, and music with soul.

On our way to
the football game,
We stopped at the tailgate
to grab some grub.

That's where the alumni and
their families hang out.
This place is filled
with so much love.

There were tents, music,
And more than enough food.
Mom and Dad were having a blast with their friends and family.
It was a whole mood.

I love watching the football game
With all the school spirit.
"Go, Eagles, go! TOUCHDOWN!"
The crowd yelled. But the rival team wouldn't hear it.

"Time for the halftime show,
Mia's favorite thing.
Me and little brother play with the band
While Mia dances and sings.

Mia cannot sit still
When the dancers
come out to groove,

Twirling in their
glittery outfits,
And dancing with
their smooth moves.

Dippin' and doin'
Mia loves to dance and wiggle.

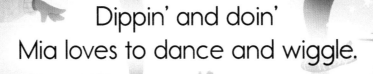

Rooting that tootie,
More than just a little.

Next, we stopped at the student union
To grab more swag.
All through the halls were pictures of alumni
And history that made me so glad.

HBCUs produce nothing but excellence,
With alumni you may know.
Let me educate you on just a few.
You're welcome in advance. Here we go!

I HAD A DREAM...

"I have a dream!"
I think you know this guy.

Martin Luther King, Jr.
was a civil rights leader.
He graduated from
Morehouse College,
and paved the way for you and I.

Lonnie Johnson.
He invented the Super Soaker water gun.
He graduated from Tuskegee University in Alabama.
He made summer so much FUN!

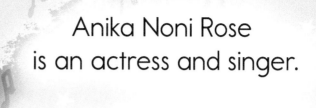

Anika Noni Rose
is an actress and singer.

She played in The Princess
and the Frog as Princess Tiana.
She went to Florida A&M University
And found her true calling, just like Moana.

The first African-American Supreme Court Justice
Went to Lincoln & Howard University.
His name is Thurgood Marshall.
He was a lawyer and Chief Counsel of the NAACP.

Another Howard University graduate, Chadwick Boseman.

So swift, kind, and clever. He played my favorite superhero, Black Panther. Wakanda forever.

Kamala Harris is among the greats.
She also graduated from Howard University
And is the first woman Vice President Of the United States!

This list goes on and on,
But this is just a taste.
There are over 100 HBCUs,
And you have the right to choose your place.

HBCUs are not just for black people.
You see all colors of the rainbow.
All races and nationalities are welcome.
Planting good seeds today, to build future leaders of tomorrow.

People come from all over the world
To be a part of the HBCU experience.
Where you understand the culture, love, and community
In a pool of brilliance.

Doctors, lawyers, inventors, scientists,
Athletes, actors, dancers, and teachers are all on the list.
Mothers, fathers, poets, and leaders.
HBCUs are the ultimate breeders!

HBCUs are important because they are big in faith and service in the community.

Helping one another, loving each other, Building us up

Just like our Fathers and Mothers.

"AAAAAAYYYYYYEE!!"
Someone yelled from across the yard.
He started stomping and howling toward us.
It was my Dad's frat brother, Mr. Bernard.

My Dad pledged Greek in college.
That means that he is in a fraternity.
He said it is a brotherhood formed around common goals.
The women also have a sisterhood called a sorority.

Greek is oh, so sweet!
They are called the Divine 9,
Which united black students as they fought for equal rights
And did community outreach, just in time.

When you join a black frat or sorority,
You become part of a rich tradition,
Where leadership, lasting friendships,
And academic excellence is the mission.

We laughed, slayed, and played all day.
With every year, we learn a bit more.
I'm so happy to be a part of this culture.
Just like eagles, we SOAR.

"Alright, it's time to go,"
Said Mom and Dad.
"No! Can we stay just a bit longer, please?"
"We'll be back, Mia. Don't sound so sad!"

After a long day of celebrating with people who treated us like family,

I was good and tired.

On our ride back,
I pictured myself in college, going higher.

What college am I going to?
I know this without a doubt.

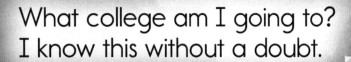

An HBCU for me, please.
This is one thing
I cannot live without.

So why do I want to go to an HBCU?
Let me put it plain and simple.
This is a place where I can be me.
Fresh cut, confidence, swag, and a dimple.

Dad asked, "Kids, did you have fun?"
We both yelled, "Of course we did!
But Dad, tell us again.
Why did you choose this school as a kid?"

Dad said, "I did it for my ancestors,
Who fought for me to have this chance.
I wanted to make them proud
Far in advance.

You know, I do not play when it comes to education,
But I'm no vulture.

I know that education is key.
So I do it for the culture."

Oh, the possibilities are ENDLESS
When it comes to a higher education.

I LOVE MY HBCUs!

What's your future aspiration?

Ask yourself these questions:

What do YOU want to be when you grow up?

HOW will you get there?

Lucky for me, HBCU is all I see, and that's what's up!

I'm smart, determined,
Focused, and pretty edgy.
Most of all, I know my worth.

I'M HBCU READY!

Made in the USA
Middletown, DE
25 April 2022

64746870R00020